THE ULTIMATE
MONTREAL CANADIENS
TRIVIA BOOK

A Collection of Amazing Trivia Quizzes
and Fun Facts for Die-Hard Habs Fans!

D1496507

Ray Walker

ISBN: 978-1-953563-18-7

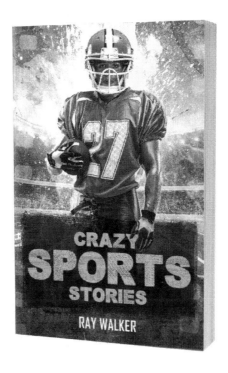

CONTENTS

Introduction 1

Chapter 1: Origins & History 3

   Quiz Time! 3

   Quiz Answers 8

   Did You Know? 9

Chapter 2: Jerseys & Numbers 12

   Quiz Time! 12

   Quiz Answers 17

   Did You Know? 18

Chapter 3: Catchy Nicknames 20

   Quiz Time! 20

   Quiz Answers 26

   Did You Know? 28

Chapter 4: The Captain Class 30

   Quiz Time! 30

   Quiz Answers 35

Did You Know? 36

Chapter 5: Statistically Speaking...........................38

Quiz Time!..38

Quiz Answers 43

Did You Know? 44

Chapter 6: The Trade Market 46

Quiz Time!..46

Quiz Answers 52

Did You Know? 53

Chapter 7: Draft Day 56

Quiz Time!..56

Quiz Answers 62

Did You Know? 63

Chapter 8: Goaltender Tidbits 65

Quiz Time!..65

Quiz Answers 71

Did You Know? 73

Chapter 9: On the Blue Line 75

Quiz Time!..75

Quiz Answers 81

Did You Know? 82

Chapter 10: Centers of Attention 85

Quiz Time!... 85

Quiz Answers 91

Did You Know? 92

Chapter 11: The Wingers Take Flight..................................... 95

Quiz Time!... 95

Quiz Answers 101

Did You Know? 103

Chapter 12: Coaches, GMs, & Owners 106

Quiz Time!..106

Quiz Answers 112

Did You Know? 113

Chapter 13: The Awards Section...116

Quiz Time!..116

Quiz Answers 122

Did You Know? 123

Conclusion 125

INTRODUCTION

Team fandom should be inspirational. Our attachment to our favorite teams should fill us with pride, excitement, loyalty, and a sense of fulfillment in knowing that we are part of a community with many other fans who feel the same way.

Montreal fans are no exception. With a rich, successful history in the National Hockey League, the Canadiens have inspired their supporters to strive for greatness with their tradition of colorful players, memorable eras, big moves, and unique moments.

This book is meant to be a celebration of those moments and an examination of the collection of interesting, impressive, or important details that allow us to understand the full stories behind the players and the team.

You may use the book as you wish. Each chapter contains 20 quiz questions in a mixture of multiple-choice and true-false formats, an answer key (Don't worry, it's on a separate page!), and a section of 10 "Did You Know? " facts about the team.

Some will use it to test themselves with the quiz questions. How much Canadiens history do you really know? How many of the finer points can you remember? Some will use it competitively (Isn't that the heart of sports?), waging contests with friends and fellow devotees to see who can lay claim to being the biggest fan. Some will enjoy it as a learning experience, gaining insight to enrich their fandom and add color to their understanding of their favorite team. Still others may use it to teach, sharing the wonderful anecdotes inside to inspire a new generation of fans to hop aboard the Habs bandwagon.

Whatever your purpose may be, we hope you enjoy delving into the amazing background of Montreal Canadiens hockey!

Oh, for the record, information and statistics in this book are current up to the beginning of 2020. The Canadiens will surely topple more records and win more awards as the seasons pass, so keep this in mind when you're watching the next game with your friends, and someone starts a conversation with "Did you know…?".

CHAPTER 1:

ORIGINS & HISTORY

QUIZ TIME!

1. In which year did the Canadiens begin playing in the National Hockey League?

   a. 1885
   b. 1909
   c. 1917
   d. 1923

2. Despite their history of success, the Canadiens nearly moved to Cleveland, Ohio, while struggling during the Great Depression.

   a. True
   b. False

3. How was the nickname "the Habs" given to the team?

   a. It was short for "Haberdashers," a term for the clothing dealers who first owned the team.
   b. It was short for "Habits," given to the team after they made a habit of winning early in franchise history.

c. It was short for "Habitants," early farmers and settlers in Quebec.

d. It was a misheard remark; the team with its wealth of talents was called "the Haves" as opposed to the "Have-Nots."

4. In which season did the Canadiens leave the historic Montreal Forum and begin to play in their new arena (the Bell Center—formerly the Molson Center)?

a. 1984

b. 1996

c. 2003

d. 2009

5. Who was the founder of the Montreal Canadiens?

a. George Kennedy

b. J. Ambrose O'Brien

c. Molson Breweries

d. Howie Morenz

6. In which season did the Canadiens earn their first-ever NHL playoff berth?

a. 1917-18

b. 1923-24

c. 1930-31

d. 1933-34

7. The Canadiens ended up playing in the Montreal Forum after two of their previous arenas had burned down.

a. True

b. False

8. How many times in their franchise history have the Canadiens won a division title?

   a. 12 times
   b. 19 times
   c. 24 times
   d. 32 times

9. Who were the first two Canadiens ever to be named as Montreal's representative on the NHL All-Star Team?

   a. Wilf Cude and Babe Siebert
   b. Elmer Lach and Maurice Richard
   c. Howie Morenz and Aurèle Joliat
   d. Émile Bouchard and Maurice Richard

10. Where do the Montreal Canadiens rank among NHL franchises when it comes to most Stanley Cup championships won?

    a. 1st
    b. 3rd
    c. Tied for 5th
    d. Tied for 8th

11. How did the Canadiens fare during their 50th anniversary season in the NHL?

    a. Missed the playoffs
    b. Lost in the first round
    c. Lost in the second round
    d. Won the Stanley Cup

12. The Montreal Forum was originally built to house an expansion hockey team, the Montreal Maroons, not the Canadiens.

    a. True
    b. False

13. Which team did Montreal face in its first-ever NHL game (which resulted in a 7-4 victory)?

    a. New York Rangers
    b. Toronto Maple Leafs
    c. Boston Bruins
    d. Ottawa Senators

14. Montreal's current top farm team plays in the American Hockey League. What is this team called?

    a. Hamilton Bulldogs
    b. St. John's IceCaps
    c. Laval Rocket
    d. Fredericton Canadiens

15. Which player scored five goals in the first-ever NHL game for the Montreal Canadiens?

    a. Joe Malone
    b. Newsy Lalonde
    c. Babe Siebert
    d. Joe Hall

16. Montreal has allowed fewer players to participate in the Winter Olympics to represent their countries than any other NHL franchise.

a. True

b. False

17. How did Montreal fare in its first-ever NHL playoff run?

    a. Lost in the first round to the Detroit Red Wings

    b. Won the Stanley Cup against the Ottawa Senators

    c. Lost in the second round to the Chicago Blackhawks

    d. Lost in the NHL Finals to the Toronto Arenas

18. When George Kennedy purchased the team from J. Ambrose O'Brien, how much did he pay for the franchise?

    a. $500

    b. $7,500

    c. $2,000

    d. $116,500

19. What is the name of the Montreal Canadiens' mascot?

    a. Gritty

    b. Habby

    c. Youppi

    d. Pucks

20. The Montreal Canadiens were formed with the intent of providing a francophone-based team as a rival to the Montreal Wanderers.

    a. True

    b. False

QUIZ ANSWERS

1. C – 1917

2. A – True

3. C – It was short for "Habitants," early farmers and settlers in Quebec.

4. B – 1996

5. B – J. Ambrose O'Brien

6. A – 1917-18

7. A – True

8. C – 24 times

9. C – Howie Morenz and Aurèle Joliat

10. A – 1st

11. D – Won the Stanley Cup

12. A – True

13. D – Ottawa Senators

14. C – Laval Rocket

15. A – Joe Malone

16. B – False

17. D – Lost in the NHL Finals to the Toronto Arenas

18. B – $7,500

19. C – Youppi

20. A – True

DID YOU KNOW?

1. Over the years, the Montreal Canadiens have been shuffled around within the NHL. They've played in the Canadian Division, the East Division, the Norris Division, the Adams Division, the Northeast Division, and the Atlantic Division. At times, they've been placed in the Wales Conference and the East Conference.

2. The Habs were not originally the only professional ice hockey team in Quebec. When they began playing, they were part of the National Hockey Association along with the Montreal Shamrocks, Montreal Wanderers, and Quebec Bulldogs.

3. The Montreal Canadiens are the franchise currently in existence that was founded before the NHL itself. They became a club in 1909 and joined the National Hockey League when it was created in 1917.

4. The Canadiens have shared their home, the Bell Center, with a few other sports tenants throughout the years. The arena has housed the Montreal Roadrunners (of RHI), the Montreal Impact (of NPSL), the Montreal Rocket (of QMJHL), and the Montreal Express (of NLL).

5. The Montreal Canadiens are the longest uninterruptedly functioning ice hockey team in the world. Established in 1909, they were created before the NHL itself.

6. The Canadiens appeared in the Stanley Cup Finals in 1919, but neither won nor lost. That year, an outbreak of Spanish flu caused the Finals to be cancelled. Player Joe Hall died from the pandemic.

7. Montreal's biggest NHL rival is generally thought to be the Toronto Maple Leafs, as the two teams are both Original Six members and compete to be thought of as Canada's favorite team, in addition to having an English vs. French component. Theirs is the oldest rivalry in NHL history. The Habs have been far more successful overall, but hold just a slim 8-7 lead in playoff series between the two teams.

8. In the beginning, before becoming a juggernaut, Montreal had mixed success. During their first decade in the NHL, Montreal appeared in three Stanley Cup Finals (winning one), but also missed the playoffs in four seasons, including three straight at one point.

9. It has always been of major importance for the Canadiens to conduct business in both French and English because they have fans who associate very strongly with each language. Official team communication is released in both languages, and at games, the first verse of "O Canada" (the national anthem) is sung in French, while the chorus is sung in English.

10. Unlike many teams, the Canadiens have an official motto. Taken from a World War I poem, it says, "To you from failing hands we throw the torch. Be yours to hold it high."

Reflective of the Habs' long and storied legacy, it is prominent in the team's dressing room and has even appeared on their jerseys at times.

CHAPTER 2:

JERSEYS & NUMBERS

QUIZ TIME!

1. When they began playing in the NHL, the Canadiens used what color scheme for their uniforms?

    a. Red and white
    b. Blue and black
    c. Red, white, and blue
    d. Green and white

2. The numbers 0 and 00 have been banned from circulation by Montreal's ownership because they are seen to represent a losing attitude.

    a. True
    b. False

3. Who was the first player to have his number retired by the Montreal Canadiens?

    a. Maurice Richard
    b. Jean Béliveau
    c. Howie Morenz
    d. Elmer Lach

4. Three legendary players have worn number 16 for the Habs. Which one of the following players did NOT wear it?

   a. Toe Blake
   b. Yvan Cournoyer
   c. Henri Richard
   d. Elmer Lach

5. Aside from their regular colors, what color did the Canadiens sport on their jerseys during their 100th anniversary celebration?

   a. Black
   b. Orange
   c. Green
   d. Grey

6. Which jersey number has proven to be most popular with Montreal, having been worn by 49 players?

   a. 3
   b. 8
   c. 12
   d. 20

7. During the 1924-25 season, Montreal wore a special jersey commemorating its championship status, which featured a large globe logo instead of their traditional "CH."

   a. True
   b. False

8. Which two players wore the highest numbered jersey (95) in Montreal franchise history?

a. Doug Gilmour and Scott Gomez

b. Sergei Berezin and Olivier Michaud

c. Stéphane Richer and Guillaume Latendresse

d. Yanic Perreault and Tom Pyatt

9. Why did star winger Maurice Richard choose to wear number 9 on his jersey?

a. He was the ninth child in his family.

b. He felt it was lucky after scoring nine goals in his first training camp with the team.

c. He chose it to match the birth weight of his daughter Huguette.

d. He was born on September 9, 1919.

10. Andrei Markov is the only Canadien ever to wear which uniform number?

a. 70

b. 79

c. 84

d. 97

11. Which jersey range has been worn by the fewest number of Montreal Canadiens players?

a. 90-99

b. 70-79

c. 50-59

d. 20-29

12. Habs icon Maurice Richard is the only Canadien to have ever worn the number 9 on his jersey.

a. True

b. False

13. Why did Habs defenseman Hal Gill choose to wear number 75 on the back of his jersey?

    a. It was a combination of his two favorite Canadiens players, Howie Morenz (7) and Bernie Geoffrion (5).

    b. When he was drafted, an analyst joked that Gill was "huge, like 7'5"!"

    c. As a young teenager, he hit 75 miles per hour during his first "hardest shot" competition.

    d. He was born in 1975.

14. How many jersey numbers have the Montreal Canadiens retired for their former players?

    a. 7

    b. 12

    c. 15

    d. 21

15. Which player competed for the Habs for just eight seasons, the shortest tenure of anyone whose number has been retired by the franchise?

    a. Jacques Plante

    b. Patrick Roy

    c. Ken Dryden

    d. Bob Gainey

16. Twenty-one players have worn the number 1 for Montreal, and every single one of them was a goaltender.

a. True

b. False

17. Lucky number 7 has been worn by five Canadiens players over the years before being retired. Which skater wore it for the longest period of time?

   a. Joe Malone

   b. Amos Arbour

   c. Henri Richard

   d. Howie Morenz

18. Who is the most recent Canadiens player to have his number retired by the club?

   a. Guy Lapointe

   b. Elmer Lach

   c. Patrick Roy

   d. Larry Robinson

19. Which number did Newsy Lalonde, who was named the first NHL captain in Canadiens history, wear on the back of his jersey?

   a. 2

   b. 4

   c. 9

   d. 11

20. The Montreal Canadiens have retired more jersey numbers than any other NHL franchise.

   a. True

   b. False

QUIZ ANSWERS

1. C – Red, white, and blue

2. B – False

3. C – Howie Morenz

4. B – Yvan Cournoyer

5. C – Green

6. D – 20

7. A – True

8. B – Sergei Berezin and Olivier Michaud

9. C – He chose it to match the birth weight of his daughter Huguette.

10. B – 79

11. A – 90-99

12. B – False

13. D – He was born in 1975.

14. C – 15

15. C – Ken Dryden

16. A – True

17. D – Howie Morenz

18. A – Guy Lapointe

19. B – 4

20. A – True

DID YOU KNOW?

1. The Canadiens' red, white, and blue "CH" logo was adopted by the club in 1917, when the franchise switched its name from "Club Athletique Canadien" to "Club de Hockey Canadien."

2. The highest number ever sported by a Canadiens goaltender is 95. In the 2001-02 season, the Habs had to rely on emergency third-string goalie Olivier Michaud to play one period (stopping all 14 shots he faced), and he donned the number 95 because it was readily available. His appearance made Michaud the youngest goaltender to ever appear for Montreal.

3. For a short period from 1944 to 1947, the classic Canadiens jersey was augmented with a large, thick, dark blue stripe running across the chest. The logo was presented on this stripe on the front, and the number was located on the stripe on the back.

4. Some numbers have proven unpopular with Montreal players through the years. Eight numbers have gone unused in franchise history. They are 50, 66, 69, 87, 96, 97, 98, and 99.

5. When Canadiens icon Henri Richard had his number 16 jersey retired by the franchise, he persuaded the team to donate all the profits from that night to have a gymnasium built at a local orphanage.

6. Montreal has retired three numbers on behalf of multiple players. Number 5 was sent to the rafters in honor of Bernie Geoffrion and Guy Lapointe, number 12 paid homage to Yvan Cournoyer and Dickie Moore, and number 16 was taken out of the rotation to celebrate Henri Richard and Elmer Lach.

7. Superstition may have scared some Canadiens away from wearing the number 13. Only six players in franchise history have chosen it for themselves, and no one has worn it for more than three years with the club.

8. Since 1936, the Canadiens have always worn blue shorts with their uniforms. Before that, they had worn brown and beige on their lower halves.

9. The original Montreal jersey had a raised blue collar on it, similar to a turtleneck. This lasted only two years before the sweaters were changed to a flat, regular neck opening.

10. Georges Vézina was the first Canadien to wear number 1 in the NHL, and has a major goaltending award trophy named after him, but the Habs have retired the number 1 in honor of a different goalie, Jacques Plante.

CHAPTER 3:

CATCHY NICKNAMES

QUIZ TIME!

1. By which franchise nickname are the Canadiens most commonly called?

    a. The Red C's
    b. The Frenchies
    c. The Red and Blue
    d. The Habs/Les Habs

2. Jean Béliveau's nickname, "Le Gros Bill" (Big Bill), was taken from the title of a French-Canadian folk song and bestowed upon him by a journalist.

    a. True
    b. False

3. The longtime home of the Habs, the Montreal Forum was also further described as which of the following?

    a. "The hallowed halls of hockey history"
    b. "The museum of ghosts and legends"
    c. "The most storied building in hockey history"
    d. "The epitome of home ice advantage"

4. Which three forwards played together in a combination known as "The Dynasty Line"?

    a. Guy Lafleur, Pete Mahovlich, and Steve Shutt
    b. Henri Richard, Yvan Cournoyer, and Toe Blake
    c. Jean Béliveau, Maurice Richard, and Bert Olmstead
    d. Saku Koivu, Alex Kovalev, and Brian Savage

5. Why was Canadiens right winger Chris Nilan nicknamed "Knuckles"?

    a. He had an annoying habit of cracking his knuckles on team bus or plane trips.
    b. He was known as an enforcer and would drop his gloves at any opportunity.
    c. He annoyed goalies by trying to develop an unpredictable "knuckleball" type shot in practice.
    d. He lived close to the team's practice arena and walked to and from practice, but wore a set of brass knuckles because the neighborhood was not the safest.

6. Which of the following defenseman was NOT a member of the Habs' heralded "Big 3" that led the team to six Stanley Cups in the 1970s?

    a. Guy Lapointe
    b. Jean-Guy Talbot
    c. Serge Savard
    d. Larry Robinson

7. Goaltender Michel "Bunny" Larocque was given his nickname for his habit of hopping quickly to his feet after sprawling for big saves.

a. True

b. False

8. Why was Habs winger Aurèle Joliat given the nicknames "Mighty Atom" and "Little Giant" by his teammates?

    a. He had a remarkable career in atom hockey, winning two scoring titles and racking up the most penalty minutes in the league.

    b. He was small in size (just 136 pounds) but played with a big heart.

    c. He won several strength competitions among players in the dressing room.

    d. He was known to be arrogant and thought very highly of himself.

9. Which of the following nicknames did NOT apply to Habs goalie Cristobal Huet?

    a. Closed Pipes

    b. The Man from France

    c. Hip-hip-hu-et

    d. CristoWall

10. Why did Canadiens fans refer to goaltender Andre Racicot as "Red Light Racicot"?

    a. He frequently made saves considered thefts, which figuratively left opposing players calling for the police.

    b. He skated out for warm-ups with a red spotlight on him to differentiate him from the other players.

    c. He received several speeding tickets on Montreal's highways.

d. He had difficulty stopping the puck, so the goal light was often flashing.

11. By which edible nickname was Montreal winger Mario Tremblay known to fans and teammates?

    a. The Strawberry Sorbet
    b. The Bionic Blueberry
    c. Wine and Cheese Man
    d. Sweet Pickles

12. Montreal forward Alexei Kovalev was nicknamed "AK-27" in reference to his initials, jersey number, and excellent shot.

    a. True
    b. False

13. 13. Which Canadiens captain was known to teammates by the nickname "Captain K"?

    a. Kirk Muller
    b. Saku Koivu
    c. Mike Keane
    d. Butch Bouchard

14. Why did teammates call Canadiens forward Joseph Bernard Andre Geoffrion by the nickname "Boom Boom"?

    a. Because he finished all of his body checks, including "one boom to knock you down and one more while you were down there."
    b. Because he souped up his fancy convertible with a sound system that thundered bass notes and drowned out conversation.

c. Because he was an originator of the slapshot, which he used to tremendous effect.

d. Because he maintained a double-barreled shotgun at his rural home, and often showed off his marksmanship to teammates.

15. Which Habs goaltender was known as "the Chicoutimi Cucumber" in a reference to his cool, calm demeanor between the pipes?

a. Jacques Plante
b. Georges Vézina
c. Patrick Roy
d. José Théodore

16. Longtime Habs defender Andrei Markov was nicknamed "The General."

a. True
b. False

17. What were Habs forwards (and brothers) Frank and Pete Mahovlich known as around the league?

a. The Hockey Maharajahs
b. Big M and Little M
c. The Passer and The Sniper
d. The Brothers Grim

18. Which Habs forward was known as "Le Petit Viking" because of his heritage and lack of height?

a. Lars Eller
b. Turner Stevenson

c. Mats Naslund

d. Chris Nilan

19. Defender Francis Bouillon was referred to by several nicknames throughout his career. Which of the following was NOT applied to Bouillon?

a. Cube

b. Frank the Tank

c. Soupy

d. The Big Warrior

20. "The French Connection" was a forward line for the Habs in the 1970s that was named after a Gene Hackman movie.

a. True

b. False

QUIZ ANSWERS

1. D – The Habs/Les Habs

2. A – True

3. C – "The most storied building in hockey history"

4. A – Guy Lafleur, Pete Mahovlich, and Steve Shutt

5. B – He was known as an enforcer and would drop his gloves at any opportunity.

6. B – Jean-Guy Talbot

7. B – False

8. B – He was small in size (just 136 pounds) but played with a big heart.

9. A – Closed Pipes

10. D – He had difficulty stopping the puck, so the goal light was often flashing.

11. B – The Bionic Blueberry

12. A – True

13. B – Saku Koivu

14. C – Because he was an originator of the slapshot, which he used to tremendous effect.

15. B – Georges Vézina

16. A – True

17. B – Big M and Little M

18. C – Mats Naslund

19. D – The Big Warrior

20. B – False

DID YOU KNOW?

1. Early-era Habs star Edouard Lalonde was given his moniker, "Newsy," because during that era most players worked other jobs, and Lalonde had spent some time laboring in a newspaper plant.

2. Although it was rumored that Habs forward Doug Gilmour got the nickname "Killer" because of his resemblance to convicted murderer Charles Manson, he actually received it from a teammate due to his remarkable intensity while playing.

3. Montreal's famed "Punch Line" of Toe Blake, Maurice Richard, and Elmer Lach sure packed a wallop on the ice. In 1944-45, they finished 1st, 2nd, and 3rd in NHL scoring—only the second time a forward line had ever achieved this.

4. Brothers Maurice and Henri Richard both became icons in Montreal Canadiens history. Maurice, known for his competitive fire, fierce power, and scoring prowess, was called "The Rocket." Henri, who was fifteen years younger and a few inches shorter, was known as "The Pocket Rocket."

5. Yvan "the Roadrunner" Cournoyer was given his alias due to the terrific speed he shared with the bird of the same name. Cournoyer credited this speed to the use of skate blades that were longer than usual.

6. At 6' 4", goaltender Ken Dryden was tall enough and skillful enough to be affectionately known as "the Four-Story Goalie" by fans, and was once referred to as "that thieving giraffe" by opponents.

7. Joseph Hector "Toe" Blake was known by his nickname almost exclusively. It was given to him by his younger sister, who pronounced his name as "Hec-toe," and was much catchier than his briefly used hockey nickname, "the Old Lamplighter."

8. Guy Lafleur was known by two nicknames. "Flower" was a literal English translation of his last name, which also spoke to the beauty of his game. "Le Demon Blond" ("the Blond Demon") was a reference to the sight of his long blond hair streaming behind him during rushes down the rink.

9. Standing 6' 4", defenseman Larry Robinson was called "Big Bird" partially for his size and partially because his bright, unruly hair resembled a *Sesame Street* character of the same name.

10. Early Canadiens star Howie Morenz was known by two nicknames: "The Stratford Streak" and "The Millville Meteor." Both were bestowed upon him because of his skating speed. Morenz was born in Millville and moved to Stratford as a teenager.

CHAPTER 4:

THE CAPTAIN CLASS

QUIZ TIME!

1. Which player was honored by being named the inaugural captain of the Montreal Canadiens in 1917?

   a. Maurice Richard
   b. Sylvio Mantha
   c. Newsy Lalonde
   d. Sprague Cleghorn

2. The Canadiens have never named a Russian, Swedish, Czech, or Slovak player as team captain.

   a. True
   b. False

3. Which captain holds the record for most points in a season while leading the Canadiens, with 96?

   a. Vincent Damphousse
   b. Jean Béliveau
   c. Yvan Cournoyer
   d. Pierre Turgeon

4. Who was the first Habs captain to win a Stanley Cup in the NHL with the team?

    a. Newsy Lalonde
    b. Sprague Cleghorn
    c. Babe Siebert
    d. Toe Blake

5. For how many of his eight seasons as captain did Butch Bouchard lead all Canadiens defensemen in scoring?

    a. 0
    b. 2
    c. 5
    d. 8

6. Which player was the oldest to wear the C for the Montreal Canadiens at 39 years old?

    a. Doug Harvey
    b. Henri Richard
    c. Jean Béliveau
    d. Maurice Richard

7. In their entire history, the Montreal Canadiens have never named a goaltender captain of the team.

    a. True
    b. False

8. One Habs leader was actually known by the nickname "Le Capitaine." Who was this?

    a. Guy Carbonneau
    b. Jean Béliveau

c. Bob Gainey

d. Saku Koivu

9. Which Canadien set the franchise record for most penalty minutes in a season by a Montreal captain?

a. Sylvio Mantha in 1929-30

b. Butch Bouchard in 1953-54

c. Maurice Richard in 1956-57

d. Chris Chelios in 1989-90

10. Two Montreal captains, Kirk Muller and Saku Koivu, are tied for the lowest plus/minus season for any Habs captain since the NHL began tracking the statistic. How low did they finish?

a. -21

b. -29

c. -40

d. -46

11. How many times since 1917 has a Canadiens captain scored 30 (or more) goals in a single season?

a. 2

b. 9

c. 18

d. 31

12. For three seasons in the 1960s, Montreal elected not to name a captain. Instead, they had a rotation of players wear an A (usually designated for assistant captains) with three sporting the letter in each game.

a. True

b. False

13. Which captain did the Canadiens trade to the St. Louis Blues to complete a deal in which they received center Jim Montgomery in return?

    a. Kirk Muller
    b. Pierre Turgeon
    c. Bob Gainey
    d. Guy Carbonneau

14. How many players who have held the Canadiens' captaincy have been elected to the Hockey Hall of Fame?

    a. 8
    b. 12
    c. 17
    d. 23

15. In which year did the Canadiens name their first captain who was not born in Canada?

    a. 1997-98
    b. 2008-09
    c. 1989-90
    d. 1990-2000

16. During their entire history, the Montreal Canadiens have elected only one defenseman to be the captain of the team.

    a. True
    b. False

17. Three well-travelled Canadiens captains (Kirk Muller, Pierre Turgeon, and Mike Keane) have played for six NHL teams, more than any other franchise leaders. Which other team did all three skate for?

    a. Dallas Stars
    b. New York Islanders
    c. Colorado Avalanche
    d. St. Louis Blues

18. Which Canadien was the youngest player in the team's history to be made captain?

    a. Saku Koivu
    b. Pierre Turgeon
    c. Toe Blake
    d. Sylvio Mantha

19. The team has had some great leaders who were never given the formal responsibility of being the Canadiens' captain. Which of these players is the only one to wear the C?

    a. Larry Robinson
    b. Serge Savard
    c. Tomáš Plekanec
    d. Jacques Lemaire

20. In brothers Maurice and Henri Richard, the Canadiens boast the two longest-serving captains (measured by seasons played while captain of the team) in NHL history.

    a. True
    b. False

QUIZ ANSWERS

1. C – Newsy Lalonde

2. A – True

3. D – Pierre Turgeon

4. B – Sprague Cleghorn

5. A – 0

6. C – Jean Béliveau

7. B – False

8. C – Bob Gainey

9. D – Chris Chelios in 1989-90

10. A – -21

11. B – 9

12. B – False

13. D – Guy Carbonneau

14. C – 17

15. C – 1989-90

16. B – False

17. A – Dallas Stars

18. D – Sylvio Mantha

19. B – Serge Savard

20. B – False

DID YOU KNOW?

1. Defenseman Émile Bouchard was the first Montreal Canadien born in Quebec to be named captain of the franchise. He took over the leadership position in 1948 and remained there until his retirement eight years later.

2. Canadiens captain Émile Bouchard was not afraid to demonstrate his leadership with rugged play when necessary. Among Montreal captains, Bouchard recorded four of the top 10 seasons with the most penalty minutes.

3. Center Henri Richard captained the Habs from 1971-75. Though he did not serve very long as captain, Richard still holds the record for most regular-season games played with the team (1,256).

4. Montreal's Bill Durnan captained the Canadiens from between the pipes in 1947-48. However, opponents were upset that Durnan's leaving the crease to argue referee calls gave his team extra, unofficial timeouts. The following year, the NHL ruled that goalies no longer had this right, and Durnan remains the last goaltender to wear a C on his sweater.

5. The Canadiens franchise has a history of French-Canadian stars and prefers to name them captain whenever such a suitable player is on their roster. These players are not only popular with fans but also better able to deal with members of the local francophone media.

6. Seven Canadiens captains have played their entire NHL careers with Montreal. Centers Jean Béliveau and Henri Richard spent 20 seasons with the franchise, defenseman Butch Bouchard played 15 seasons there, and goaltender Bill Durnan stayed with the team for all of his 7 years.

7. A few players have worn the C for Montreal on an interim basis without being credited for it in the history books. Larry Robinson did so during an injury to Bob Gainey, and Shayne Corson and Alexei Kovalev both took over the mantle when Saku Koivu was unavailable to the team.

8. Widely acknowledged to be the team's greatest captain ever, Jean Béliveau led the team to five Stanley Cups during his tenure. Not only did he provide steady leadership off the ice, but also paced the team in points during his last championship season, despite being nearly 40 years old.

9. Current Habs captain Shea Weber was traded to the Canadiens from the Nashville Predators, and in 2018, he became the 30th captain of the franchise.

10. Two players are tied for the longest tenure as Canadiens captain. Franchise icon Jean Béliveau led the team for 10 years, and this was later matched when Saku Koivu spent 10 of his 14 years with the club wearing the C. Koivu was the first European captain in Montreal's history.

CHAPTER 5:

STATISTICALLY SPEAKING

QUIZ TIME!

1. What is Montreal's franchise record for most victories in a single regular season?

   a. 50 wins
   b. 53 wins
   c. 58 wins
   d. 60 wins

2. No one in Canadiens history is within 100 assists of Guy Lafleur at the top of Montreal's record book.

   a. True
   b. False

3. Four goalies have recorded over 250 career wins for the Canadiens. Which one of them has the most?

   a. Ken Dryden
   b. Patrick Roy
   c. Jacques Plante
   d. Carey Price

4. Which two players are tied atop the Canadiens' single-season leaderboard in goals scored, with 60?

    a. Bernie Geoffrion and Stéphane Richer
    b. Maurice Richard and Jean Béliveau
    c. Steve Shutt and Guy Lafleur
    d. Elmer Lach and Alexei Kovalev

5. Which Hab really made his shots count, showing his accuracy with the highest career shooting percentage for the team?

    a. Stéphan Lebeau
    b. Yvon Lambert
    c. Mark Hunter
    d. Pierre Larouche

6. The most penalty minutes recorded by a Canadien is 358. Who holds this club record?

    a. Chris Nilan
    b. Lyle Odelein
    c. Maurice Richard
    d. Donald Brashear

7. Because of his longevity and high ice-time, defenseman Larry Robinson leads the Canadiens in all-time goals on-ice for AND all-time goals on-ice against.

    a. True
    b. False

8. Which goaltender holds the Montreal record for most wins in a single season, with 44?

a. Jacques Plante

b. Bill Durnan

c. Ken Dryden

d. Carey Price

9. Which Hab has played more NHL games with the franchise than any other player?

a. Andrei Markov

b. Henri Richard

c. Jean Béliveau

d. Bob Gainey

10. The iconic Maurice Richard is Montreal's all-time leader in goals scored. How many did he score?

a. 487

b. 531

c. 544

d. 602

11. Who holds the single-season Canadiens record for points per game at 1.70?

a. Newsy Lalonde

b. Guy Lafleur

c. Frank Mahovlich

d. Pete Mahovlich

12. No player ranks in the Canadiens' top 10 in career even-strength goals, power-play goals, and shorthanded goals.

a. True

b. False

13. Which Canadiens defenseman has recorded the most points while playing with the club?

    a. Andrei Markov
    b. Doug Harvey
    c. Serge Savard
    d. Larry Robinson

14. On the Canadiens' top 10 list for points scored by a player in a season, how many times does forward Guy Lafleur's name appear?

    a. 1
    b. 4
    c. 6
    d. 10

15. How many Canadiens have fired over 3,000 shots on net for the club during their careers?

    a. 1
    b. 2
    c. 3
    d. 6

16. Defenseman Larry Robinson posted a +120 rating during the 1976-77 season, which remains a franchise record and is higher than any other NHL player except Bobby Orr.

    a. True
    b. False

17. Which Canadien recorded the highest career plus/minus rating with the Canadiens, with +730, which is also the NHL record?

a. Serge Savard

b. Henri Richard

c. Larry Robinson

d. Chris Chelios

18. Which Canadien recorded the most game-winning goals for the team, with 94?

a. Guy Lafleur

b. Maurice Richard

c. Henri Richard

d. Aurèle Joliat

19. Which two teammates posted the highest combined point total in a season for the Canadiens?

a. Mats Naslund and Bobby Smith in 1985-86

b. Bernie Geoffrion and Jean Béliveau in 1960-61

c. Pete Mahovlich and Guy Lafleur in 1974-75

d. Guy Lafleur and Steve Shutt in 1976-77

20. Goalie Jacques Plante's 1961-62 season is the benchmark in terms of shots faced, as he faced 2,160; the only time a Canadiens goaltender has seen more than 2,150 shots in a season.

a. True

b. False

QUIZ ANSWERS

1. D – 60 wins

2. B – False

3. D – Carey Price

4. C – Steve Shutt and Guy Lafleur

5. C – Mark Hunter

6. A – Chris Nilan

7. A – True

8. D – Carey Price

9. B – Henri Richard

10. C – 544

11. A – Newsy Lalonde

12. A – True

13. D – Larry Robinson

14. C – 6

15. C – 3

16. A – True

17. C – Larry Robinson

18. A – Guy Lafleur

19. D – Guy Lafleur and Steve Shutt in 1976-77

20. A – True

DID YOU KNOW?

1. Three players have scored more than 1,000 points with the Canadiens franchise. Henri Richard and Jean Béliveau reached the mark through talent and longevity, as they each played 20 seasons with the Habs. Guy Lafleur surpassed them both, though, scoring more points in only 14 seasons with the team.

2. Canadiens icon Guy Lafleur ranks 7th on the all-time list for most points per game in the NHL, with 1.20. Not too far behind is Denis Savard, whose 1.12 ties him for 11th overall all-time.

3. Not counting seasons shortened by a lockout, the 2014-15 Canadiens were the stingiest version of the club to take the ice since the NHL moved to an 82-game season. They allowed only 189 goals against during the entire year.

4. Forward Guy Carbonneau was a force on the penalty kill for the Canadiens, scoring 28 shorthanded goals for the team, including 8 in 1983-84 alone. Both are franchise records.

5. Maurice Richard often scored in bunches, recording 26 of Montreal's 412 hat tricks (scoring three goals in the same game). He occasionally went beyond three goals and twice notched five in a game, including all five in a 5-1 victory over the Toronto Maple Leafs in 1944.

6. The Habs have had many tough players who were not afraid to stick up for themselves over the years, but none did so more often than right winger Chris Nilan. Nilan's career penalty minutes with Montreal (2,248) is far and away the team's most. Lyle Odelein sits a distant second with 1,367.

7. Despite many years of tough competition, Carey Price dominates the Canadiens' record books for goaltenders. He leads the franchise in wins, losses, shots against, goals against, saves, and minutes played.

8. The most recent time the Canadiens scored more than 300 goals in a season was 1992-93, when they tallied 326. This was exceptional, but still far below their franchise record of 387, set in 1976-77.

9. The deadliest Hab on the power play was center Jean Béliveau. He scored a team record 173 goals with the man advantage, 21 more than winger Yvon Cournoyer, who was on the same unit as Béliveau for several years in the 1960s.

10. In 1978-79, Guy Lafleur fired 342 shots on net, establishing the Canadiens' record for most shots taken by one player in a single season. He scored 52 times, which was good for a shooting percentage of about 15%; five percent lower than the year before, when he scored 60 goals on just 305 shots.

CHAPTER 6:

THE TRADE MARKET

QUIZ TIME!

1. The very first NHL trade ever made by the Montreal Canadiens occurred on November 28, 1918, when the Habs received some financial considerations from the Ottawa Senators. Which player did they give up in return?

   a. Jacques Plante
   b. Newsy Lalonde
   c. Tommy Smith
   d. Michel Savard

2. The Canadiens acquired Hall of Fame goaltenders Jacques Plante, Patrick Roy, and Ken Dryden in trades with other teams.

   a. True
   b. False

3. In 2018, the Habs traded captain Max Pacioretty to the Vegas Golden Knights. What did they receive in return?

   a. Shea Weber, Jesperi Kotkaniemi, and a 4th round pick
   b. Two 1st round draft choices, in 2018 and 2019

c. Max Domi, Joel Armia, a 4th round pick, and a 7th round pick

    c. Max Domi, Joel Armia, a 4th round pick, and a 7th round pick

    d. Tomas Tatar, Nick Suzuki, and a 2nd round pick

4. In 1991, Montreal made a trade with the New Jersey Devils that worked out well for both teams. Within the next few years, both of the primary players involved would win Stanley Cups with their new franchises. Who was swapped for whom in this deal?

    a. Kirk Muller for Stéphane Richer

    b. Vincent Damphousse for Shayne Corson

    c. Pierre Turgeon for Kirk Muller

    d. Shayne Corson for Pierre Turgeon

5. Which useful Canadiens player was NOT included in the deal that saw Montreal acquire Hall of Fame forward Mark Recchi from the Philadelphia Flyers?

    a. Gilbert Dionne

    b. John LeClair

    c. Mikael Renberg

    d. Éric Desjardins

6. One of the Canadiens' best trades saw them acquire center Bobby Smith in exchange for center Keith Acton, right wing Mark Napier, and a 3rd round pick. Which team regretted making that deal with Montreal?

    a. Detroit Red Wings

    b. Toronto Maple Leafs

    c. Winnipeg Jets

    d. Minnesota North Stars

7. Montreal has completed more trades with the St. Louis Blues than with any other NHL franchise.

a. True

b. False

8. In what year did the Canadiens first make a trade for "future considerations"?

a. 1918

b. 1922

c. 1928

d. 1933

9. Which of the following teams have the Montreal Canadiens NOT completed a trade with?

a. Pittsburgh Pirates

b. Detroit Cougars

c. Seattle Comets

d. New York Americans

10. Who did the Montreal Canadiens select with the 20th overall draft pick in 1971, acquired by the team in a deal that sent Dick Duff to the Los Angeles Kings?

a. Guy Lafleur

b. Larry Robinson

c. Serge Savard

d. Steve Shutt

11. In 1963, the Canadiens traded longtime netminder and future Hall-of-Famer Jacques Plante. They received another goalie in return, who luckily went on to become a

Hall-of-Famer himself. Which decorated player did they obtain to play between the pipes in this deal?

a. Gump Worsley
b. Rogie Vachon
c. Ken Dryden
d. Terry Sawchuk

12. Montreal has NEVER in its history completed a trade with the Columbus Blue Jackets.

a. True
b. False

13. Who did the Canadiens acquire from the New York Islanders in the 1995 deal where they gave up defenseman Mathieu Schneider, center Craig Darby, and winger Kirk Muller?

a. Murray Baron and Shayne Corson
b. Claude Lemieux and Jean-Jacques Daigneault
c. Vladimir Malakhov and Pierre Turgeon
d. Alexei Emelin and Stéphane Quintal

14. Who did the Habs give up in 2017 to acquire French-Canadian forward Jonathan Drouin from the Tampa Bay Lightning?

a. Defenseman Jared Tinordi
b. Defenseman Mikhail Sergachev
c. Forward Zack Kassian
d. Defenseman Josh Gorges

15. Over a 10-day period in 1938, the Montreal Canadiens

made six separate trades with the rival Montreal Maroons. How many players did the Canadiens acquire?

a. 0

b. 6

c. 11

d. 19

16. One trade that did not work out well for either team saw Montreal swap Paul Bibeault to Chicago for George Allen. Less than a year after the deal, the teams traded each player back to the other team.

a. True

b. False

17. Who did the Montreal Canadiens give up in 1990 to get French-Canadian center Denis Savard from the Chicago Blackhawks?

a. Chris Chelios

b. Claude Lemieux

c. Petr Svoboda

d. Russ Courtnall

18. During the 1988 season, the Habs traded two of their toughest players away to the New York Rangers and Toronto Maple Leafs. Which two enforcers did they deal?

a. Dale Hunter and Bob Probert

b. Mark Hunter and Stu Grimson

c. George Parros and Hal Gill

d. Chris Nilan and John Kordic

19. On November 27, 1920, the Canadiens completed their first-ever trade(s) involving three teams, acquiring Dave Ritchie, Harry Mummery, Jack McDonald, Joe Matte, and Goldie Prodgers. The team then sent out Prodgers and Matte, along with Jack Coughlin, Harry Cameron, and a loan of Billy Coutu. Who were the other two teams involved in the complicated dealings?

    a. Quebec Bulldogs and Montreal Wanderers
    b. Boston Bruins and New York Rangers
    c. Toronto Arenas and Hamilton Tigers
    d. Toronto Maple Leafs and Detroit Red Wings

20. In the 1940s, Montreal made a trade with the financially struggling Detroit Red Wings that involved not just players and cash, but also the transfer of the team bus.

    a. True
    b. False

QUIZ ANSWERS

1. C – Tommy Smith

2. B – False

3. D – Tomas Tatar, Nick Suzuki, and a 2nd round pick

4. A – Kirk Muller for Stéphane Richer

5. C – Mikael Renberg

6. D – Minnesota North Stars

7. B – False

8. D – 1933

9. C – Seattle Comets

10. B – Larry Robinson

11. A – Gump Worsley

12. B – False

13. C – Vladimir Malakhov and Pierre Turgeon

14. B – Defenseman Mikhail Sergachev

15. A – 0

16. A – True

17. A – Chris Chelios

18. D – Chris Nilan and John Kordic

19. C – Toronto Arenas and Hamilton Tigers

20. B – False

DID YOU KNOW?

1. Interestingly, four of the Canadiens' first five NHL trades involved center George "Goldie" Prodgers. In December 1919, he was acquired from the Quebec Bulldogs. He was then dealt to the Toronto Arenas in January 1920. The Habs reacquired him briefly in November 1920, only to flip him to the Hamilton Tigers the very same day.

2. During their history, the Canadiens have traded for some famous Hall of Fame names. Unfortunately, they did not get the players who made the names famous. Montreal has dealt for not-quite superstars Rene (not Ray) Bourque, Murray (not Glenn) Anderson, Jim (not Gary) Roberts, and Gerry (not Logan) Couture.

3. One of the biggest blockbusters in recent Habs history occurred on June 29, 2016, when they sent star defenseman P.K. Subban to the Nashville Predators for another star defenseman, Shea Weber. The Canadiens received some backlash because of Weber's large contract and advanced age, but Weber went on to become Montreal's captain and played very well.

4. Montreal and Chicago have a rich history of trades throughout the years. Significant names moved between the two teams include Al MacNeil, Denis Savard, Chris Chelios, Jeff Hackett, Dave Manson, Jocelyn Thibault, Stéphane Quintal, Sergei Samsonov, and Andrew Shaw.

5. Forward thinking general manager Sam Pollock made a couple of deals to land French-Canadian superstar Guy Lafleur. First, he acquired a draft pick one year in advance from the struggling Golden Seals expansion team, who needed immediate help. Then, a year later, he dealt Ralph Backstrom to the Los Angeles Kings. Backstrom helped the Kings stay out of the league basement, assuring that the Golden Seal draft pick became the 1st overall choice, and indirectly landing Lafleur in Montreal.

6. Canadiens center Vincent Damphousse was traded midflight on trade deadline day in 1999. With the team on its plane en route to Edmonton, Damphousse was dealt to the San Jose Sharks. All of the players disembarked as usual — except for Damphousse, who stayed on board and flew back to Montreal before joining his new team.

7. One of the worst trades made by the Canadiens occurred in 1995 when they sent star goalie Patrick Roy and captain Mike Keane to the Colorado Avalanche for Andrei Kovalenko, Martin Rucinsky, and Jocelyn Thibault. Roy had been upset about being left in the net during a blowout loss and demanded a trade. He went on to win two Stanley Cups and a Conn Smythe Trophy with the Avalanche.

8. A blunder was made by general manager Irving Grundman in 1982, when he sent defenseman Rod Langway (along with three other players) to the Washington Capitals for defenseman Rick Green and center Ryan Walter. Green and Walter were okay for the

Habs, but Langway immediately won two Norris Trophies and ended up in the Hall of Fame.

9. Montreal once dealt a future Hall-of-Famer to the Minnesota North Stars for cash and a future draft pick. Of course, Glen Sather, the player they dealt, made the Hall of Fame for his work as a coach and general manager. Sather only recorded 19 points as a player with the North Stars.

10. The largest trade (by number of assets) ever completed by the Habs was consummated in 1985 with the St. Louis Blues. Montreal acquired five draft picks (in the 1st, 2nd, 4th, 5th, and 6th rounds), while giving up Michael Dark, Mark Hunter, and four draft picks (in the 2nd, 3rd, 5th, and 6th rounds).

CHAPTER 7:

DRAFT DAY

QUIZ TIME!

1. The Canadiens had a fantastic draft in 1984, as all of their first four selections went on to play over 1,000 games in the NHL. Of the successful foursome, who played the most of those games for the Habs?

    a. Defenseman Petr Svoboda
    b. Left winger Shayne Corson
    c. Right winger Stéphane Richer
    d. Goaltender Patrick Roy

2. The Montreal Canadiens have never held the 1st overall pick in the NHL Draft in the entire history of the franchise.

    a. True
    b. False

3. How high did Montreal select defenseman Francois Beauchemin in the 1998 NHL Entry Draft?

    a. 1st round, 5th overall
    b. 2nd round, 43rd overall

c. 3rd round, 75th overall

d. 7th round, 222nd overall

4. Which goaltender did the Canadiens select highest in the NHL Entry Draft, using a 1st overall pick to add the netminder to their team?

   a. Carey Price

   b. Phil Myre

   c. Michel Plasse

   d. Michel Larocque

5. Who was the first player ever selected by the Habs in the NHL Entry Draft?

   a. Defenseman Rodney Presswood

   b. Defenseman Jean-Guy Talbot

   c. Goalie Phil Myre

   d. Left winger Garry Monahan

6. Which player who was drafted by the Canadiens went on to score the most NHL points for another team?

   a. John LeClair

   b. Andrew Cassels

   c. Chris Chelios

   d. Mathieu Schneider

7. Montreal has drafted precisely seven players who have played a single game in the NHL, and these players have totaled one point and two penalty minutes among them.

   a. True

   b. False

8. The Canadiens have mined the QMJHL for talent frequently in the NHL Entry Draft, and have selected 19 players from one specific QMJHL team, more than they have chosen from any other squad. Which team was it?

   a. Chicoutimi Saguencens
   b. Shawinigan Cataractes
   c. Cape Breton Eagles
   d. Montreal Bleu Blanc Rouge/Juniors/Rocket/Junior Hockey Club

9. Fan favorite P.K. Subban was selected in the 2nd round by the Montreal Canadiens in 2007. Which junior league did he play in?

   a. Quebec Major Junior Hockey League
   b. Western Hockey League
   c. Ontario Hockey League
   d. NCAA Hockey League

10. Who was the first player ever drafted by the Canadiens who did not play for a Canadian junior team?

   a. Center Lynn Powis from Denver
   b. Defenseman Greg Hubick from Minnesota-Duluth
   c. Defenseman Robert Brown from Boston University
   d. Defenseman Rick Wilson from North Dakota

11. The Vegas Golden Knights selected which Montreal Canadien in the 2017 Expansion Draft, then traded him for a draft pick before he ever played a game with the franchise?

a. Forward Paul Byron

b. Forward Pierre-Édouard Bellemare

c. Defenseman Jordie Benn

d. Defenseman Alexei Emelin

12. The Canadiens have selected 1st overall in the NHL Draft five times, which is more than any other franchise in NHL history.

a. True

b. False

13. The Canadiens struck out mightily in the 1999 NHL Draft, selecting nine skaters who scored a total of how many NHL goals?

a. 0 goals

b. 4 goals

c. 9 goals

d. 32 goals

14. Montreal legend Ken Dryden always assumed he had been drafted by the Canadiens and did not find out until nearly a decade after the fact that he had been selected by which team in the 1964 NHL Entry Draft?

a. Toronto Maple Leafs

b. Boston Bruins

c. Detroit Red Wings

d. New York Rangers

15. Solid center Doug Wickenheiser was drafted by Montreal 1st overall in the 1980 NHL Entry Draft. In that draft, the

Habs passed on which French-Canadian center who would play twice as many games and score over four times as many goals?

a. Marcel Dionne
b. Pierre Turgeon
c. Denis Savard
d. Claude Loiselle

16. When Montreal most recently hosted the NHL Entry Draft in 2009, they used their 1st round pick (18th overall) on French-Canadian center Louis Leblanc in front of the hometown crowd.

a. True
b. False

17. Up to and including the 2019 NHL Entry Draft, how many player selections have the Montreal Canadiens made in their history?

a. 302 selections
b. 317 selections
c. 486 selections
d. 599 selections

18. Which position has Montreal traditionally put a premium on, by drafting it most frequently when they've held a top 10 overall draft pick?

a. Left wing
b. Center
c. Goalie
d. Defense

19. What is the lowest position in the draft that the Canadiens have selected a player who would go on to make the Hockey Hall of Fame?

   a. 28th overall
   b. 51st overall
   c. 130th overall
   d. 207th overall

20. In the 1968 NHL Entry Draft, Montreal selected 1st, 2nd, and 3rd overall. Sadly, none of their three draft choices ever scored an NHL goal.

   a. True
   b. False

QUIZ ANSWERS

1. B – Left winger Shayne Corson

2. B – False

3. C – 3rd round, 75th overall

4. C – Michel Plasse

5. D – Left winger Garry Monahan

6. B – Andrew Cassels

7. A – True

8. D – Montreal Bleu Blanc Rouge/Juniors/Rocket/Junior Hockey Club

9. C – Ontario Hockey League

10. A – Center Lynn Powis from Denver

11. D – Defenseman Alexei Emelin

12. A – True

13. B – 4 goals

14. B – Boston Bruins

15. C – Denis Savard

16. A – True

17. D – 599 selections

18. A – Left wing

19. B – 51st overall

20. A – True

DID YOU KNOW?

1. Between 1977 and 1981, Montreal enjoyed a stretch in which they selected at least one player per year who lasted 1,000 games in the NHL. During those years, they hit on Gordie Roberts, Keith Acton, Guy Carbonneau, Craig Ludwig, and Chris Chelios.

2. When the Iron Curtain fell, the Canadiens waded slowly into the newfound player pool, selecting just two Russians and two Czechs, in the 1990-93 Entry Drafts.

3. In 1983, the Habs drafted center Alfie Turcotte with the 17th overall pick. Turcotte matched his draft position, scoring exactly 17 NHL goals. Surely, Montreal had hoped for a few more from a 1st round selection.

4. From 1963 through 1984, the NHL Draft was held every year in Montreal, at a mixture of the Queen Elizabeth Hotel, Mount Royal Hotel, Montreal Forum, and NHL Montreal Office. In 1985, it moved to Toronto for the year, but returned to Montreal again in 1986 and 1988.

5. The first Canadiens draft pick who went on to play 1,000 NHL games was right winger Guy Lafleur, in 1971. This came almost a decade after the entry draft began in 1963, but the Habs made up for lost time in that 1971 Draft by selecting defenseman Larry Robinson, who also cracked the 1,000-game mark with the club.

6. Shrewd general manager Sam Pollock knew that in 1971

two French-Canadian superstars (Guy Lafleur and Marcel Dionne) would be available in the NHL Draft. Over a year before this draft, he traded his (relatively low) 1970 1st round draft pick to the lowly California Golden Seals for their 1971 pick, which turned out to be 1st overall. The Habs selected Lafleur, and he flourished in Montreal.

7. The largest Habs draft class ever was selected in 1977, when the team drafted a whopping 27 players over the course of the draft. Sixteen of these players never made it to the NHL, three played just a handful of games, and the other eight made various significant contributions, led by defensemen Rod Langway and Gordie Roberts.

8. Montreal has drafted four players who went on to record over 2,000 penalty minutes in the NHL. These players came from a wide spectrum; left winger Shayne Corson was taken in the 1st round (8th overall), defender Chris Chelios came in the 2nd round (40th overall), fellow defender Lyle Odelein was grabbed in the 7th round (141st overall), and right winger Chris Nilan had to wait until the 19th round (231st overall) to hear his name called.

9. The Canadiens drafted two foreign goalies in the 2003 NHL Draft. Sixth round Swedish netminder Chris Heino-Lindberg did not pan out, but the Habs found a gem in 9th round Slovak Jaroslav Halák, who is still playing in the NHL to this day.

10. The latest pick the Canadiens have made in the NHL Draft was American center Russell Guzior, with the 281st overall pick in 1993. Guzior never played an NHL game.

CHAPTER 8:

GOALTENDER TIDBITS

QUIZ TIME!

1. Who was the regular starting goalie for Montreal during the team's fairly successful first season in the NHL?

   a. Georges Vézina

   b. George Hainsworth

   c. Bill Durnan

   d. Gerry McNeil

2. For a 15-year period between 1910 and 1925, Georges Vézina was the only goaltender to play for the Montreal Canadiens.

   a. True

   b. False

3. Which goaltender recorded the most career shutouts while with the Montreal Canadiens?

   a. Ken Dryden

   b. Jacques Plante

   c. George Hainsworth

   d. Carey Price

4. In addition to lending his name to the NHL's annual trophy for the best goaltender, what else did Georges Vézina accomplish in his career?

   a. Became the first goalie to wear a mask and the first to play every game for his team for a season
   b. Became the first goalie to score a goal and the first to fight an opposing goaltender
   c. Became the first goalie to stop a penalty shot attempt and the first to sign a six-figure NHL contract
   d. Became the first goalie to record a shutout and the first to notch an assist on a goal

5. Ex-Habs goalie Ken Dryden served as a Canadian Member of Parliament from 2004-11 with which political party?

   a. Reform Party
   b. Parti Quebecois
   c. Progressive Conservative Party
   d. Liberal Party

6. Which of the following is NOT a record held by Montreal legend George Hainsworth?

   a. Most shutouts recorded in a single season (22)
   b. Lowest goals-against average posted in a single season (0.92)
   c. Highest save percentage in a single season (.993)
   d. NHL playoff consecutive shutout streak record (270 minutes, 8 seconds)

7. It is a Canadiens tradition for every goaltender to tap both posts and the crossbar with his stick following the warm-up before a game.

a. True

b. False

8. Which of the following is NOT a true fact about quirky Habs goaltender Carey Price?

    a. In 2016-17, Price entered the record books as the first NHL goalie to ever win his first 10 games of the season.

    b. Price owns homes in Montreal, Kelowna, and Hawaii.

    c. Growing up, Price lived far from the closest organized hockey team, so his father purchased a plane to fly him to games and practices.

    d. Price has a First Nation lineage through his mother's side.

9. Which Canadiens goaltender holds the franchise record for most saves in a single game, with 53?

    a. Ken Dryden

    b. Michel Larocque

    c. Brian Hayward

    d. Carey Price

10. Which Habs goalie was the first NHL netminder to play in an outdoor game, the 2003 Heritage Classic, which he won 4-3 while sporting a toque over his helmet?

    a. Patrick Roy

    b. Carey Price

    c. José Théodore

    d. Jeff Hackett

11. Which of the following did goaltender Steve Penney NOT get after the Canadiens won the Stanley Cup in 1986?

a. A Stanley Cup ring

b. Included in the team picture

c. Traded to Winnipeg

d. His name on the Stanley Cup

12. Habs legend Georges Vézina left a game after throwing up blood during the intermission, was subsequently taken to hospital, diagnosed with tuberculosis, and passed away a few months later.

a. True

b. False

13. Which Vezina-winning goalie served as Ken Dryden's backup in Montreal and filled in when Dryden was away from the team in 1974?

a. Rogie Vachon

b. Michel Larocque

c. Gump Worsley

d. Jocelyn Thibault

14. How long did Montreal netminder Bill Durnan's shutout streak of 309 minutes, 21 seconds remain the NHL record?

a. 12 years

b. 28 years

c. 40 years

d. 55 years

15. Which of these accomplishments did Montreal's Ken Dryden NOT achieve the season before he won the Calder Trophy as the NHL's rookie of the year?

a. Won the Stanley Cup

b. Did not lose a single regular-season game

c. Won the Conn Smythe Trophy

d. Posted 10 shutouts in the NHL

16. Former Canadiens goalie Denis Herron was the first goaltender in professional hockey to score a goal.

a. True

b. False

17. Which Montreal goaltender literally wrote the book *Goaltending*, which became a top seller in both English and French for about 25 years?

a. Rogie Vachon

b. Ken Dryden

c. Gerry McNeil

d. Jacques Plante

18. Montreal goaltender Carey Price played in the 2014 Winter Olympics for which team?

a. United States of America

b. Canada

c. France

d. Sweden

19. Which of the following statements about Habs goalie Patrick Roy is NOT true?

a. He is the only player to win the Conn Smythe Trophy for two different franchises.

b. He is the only player in the league's history to take home the Conn Smythe Trophy three times.

c. He is the only player to win the Conn Smythe Trophy as a member of the losing team.

d. He is the only NHL player to win the Conn Smythe Trophy in difference decades.

20. Prior to wearing a mask while playing, Habs goalie Jacques Plante used to wear a toque on his head between the pipes.

a. True

b. False

QUIZ ANSWERS

1. A – Georges Vézina

2. A – True

3. C – George Hainsworth

4. D – Became the first goalie to record a shutout and the first to notch an assist on a goal

5. D – Liberal Party

6. C – Highest save percentage in a single season (.993)

7. B – False

8. B – Price owns homes in Montreal, Kelowna, and Hawaii.

9. D – Carey Price

10. C – José Théodore

11. D – His name on the Stanley Cup

12. A – True

13. B – Michel Larocque

14. D – 55 years

15. D – Posted 10 shutouts in the NHL

16. B – False

17. D – Jacques Plante

18. B – Canada

19. C – He is the only player to win the Conn Smythe Trophy as a member of the losing team.

20. A – True

DID YOU KNOW?

1. Montreal's Bill Durnan was ambidextrous, and wore gloves specifically designed to allow him to catch with either of his hands while switching his stick between left and right.

2. Habs goalie Jacques Plante was the first netminder in the NHL to wear a mask regularly while playing between the pipes. During the 1959-60 season, coach Toe Blake finally relented and allowed Plante to wear the mask after a shot to the face broke his nose during a game. Plante wore the mask for an unbeaten stretch of 18 games. The streak was broken the night Blake made him remove the mask, so it quickly returned for good after the loss.

3. Jacques Plante was also the first goalie to play the puck outside of his goalie crease. Some coaches were unhappy about this, but Plante felt that it kept the puck away from the opposing team, and continued to do it.

4. One Montreal goaltender has been credited with a goal in an NHL game. On January 2, 2001, José Théodore took a shot at the empty net after the New York Islanders pulled goalie John Vanbiesbrouck. With nine seconds left, the puck went in to put the Habs up 3-0.

5. Canadiens goalie Lorne "Gump" Worsley became something of a cult figure in Canadian popular culture. Not one, but two bands have written songs about him

(Huevos Rancheros recorded "Gump Worsley's Lament," and The Weakerthans wrote "Elegy for Gump Worsley"), and a third titled an album after him (Sons of Freedom's *Gump*).

6. Habs goaltender Ken Dryden was an intellectual as well. At one point, he took a year off from the NHL to earn his law degree from McGill University in Montreal. After his playing career, he became an author, commentator, politician, teacher, and executive.

7. Nine goalies who have played for the Canadiens have been enshrined in the Hall of Fame. The most recent was Rogie Vachon, who was elected in 2016.

8. Montreal goalie Ken Dryden played his first NHL game against his brother, Dave Dryden of the Buffalo Sabres. It remains the only instance where brothers have ever faced each other as goaltenders.

9. Montreal icon Patrick Roy is well known for making the butterfly style of goaltending more widespread. Roy would go down to his knees on the ice to let his pads block the lower portion of the net more effectively.

10. During the 1951 Stanley Cup playoffs, Habs goalie Gerry McNeil posted 214 straight minutes of shutout hockey against the Detroit Red Wings, included 62 saves in one lengthy overtime game, prompting Detroit's GM Jack Adams to call it "the greatest goaltending this team has ever faced."

CHAPTER 9:

ON THE BLUE LINE

QUIZ TIME!

1. Montreal's Larry Robinson made the playoffs in 20 consecutive seasons, an NHL record he shares with which other defenseman?

   a. Boston's Bobby Orr
   b. Winnipeg's Teppo Numminen
   c. Detroit's Nicklas Lidstrom
   d. Toronto's Börje Salming

2. Defender Stéphane Quintal moved on from his playing career with Montreal, and is currently the NHL's senior vice president of player safety.

   a. True
   b. False

3. Habs defensemen Émile and Pierre Bouchard share which record for a father/son duo in the NHL?

   a. Most combined seasons played with the same franchise (22)

b. Most penalty minutes recorded by a family (4,083)

c. Fewest games missed due to injury in combined careers (74)

d. Most Stanley Cups won by a father and son (9)

4. Ageless wonder and ex-Canadien Chris Chelios holds many NHL records for his longevity. Which of the following does NOT belong to him?

a. Most NHL games played by a defenseman

b. Most NHL seasons played (tied with Gordie Howe)

c. Most penalty minutes recorded by a defenseman

d. Most career NHL playoff games played

5. Offensive defenseman Patrice Brisebois tried his hand at which other professional sport after his retirement from the NHL in 2009?

a. PGA golf

b. NASCAR racing

c. Figure skating

d. Professional poker tour

6. Which defender has played the most games for the Canadiens?

a. Andrei Markov

b. Larry Robinson

c. Serge Savard

d. Doug Harvey

7. After a lengthy and one-sided fight featuring Montreal tough guy Émile Bouchard, the NHL for the first time made it the duty of referees to break up fights on the ice.

a. True

b. False

8. Which Montreal player is the only NHL defenseman to record a hat trick in a Stanley Cup Finals game, scoring all three goals in a 3-2 Montreal victory?

a. Larry Robinson

b. Guy Lapointe

c. Serge Savard

d. Éric Desjardins

9. About which Habs defenseman did noted hockey analyst Don Cherry say, "[He] should be captain of the Canadiens, there's no doubt in my mind. He's a captain's captain…he's exceptional. Look up the word leader in the dictionary and you'll find [his] picture."?

a. Josh Gorges

b. Shea Weber

c. P.K. Subban

d. Andrei Markov

10. What do fan-favorite Canadiens defenseman P.K. Subban's initials actually stand for?

a. Patrick Kennedy

b. Pernell Karl

c. Pierre Kurtis

d. Penalty Killer

11. Defenseman Émile "Butch" Bouchard played his entire NHL career with the Montreal Canadiens after they brought him up in 1941. How long did that career last?

a. 8 seasons

b. 10 seasons

c. 12 seasons

d. 15 seasons

12. Habs defender Tom Johnson was born in Manitoba, Canada, but was one of the few players who had a family ancestry from Iceland.

a. True

b. False

13. Canadiens mainstay Andrei Markov played over 900 NHL games with the club. Where does he rank in all-time games played for Montreal?

a. 2nd

b. 6th

c. 11th

d. 15th

14. Which current Canadiens defenseman has the longest tenure in Montreal?

a. Karl Alzner

b. Shea Weber

c. Jeff Petry

d. Brett Kulak

15. The Habs scouted and drafted defender Craig Ludwig from an American college team that won two National Championships and featured nine future NHL players. Which college team did Ludwig play for?

a. University of Minnesota Golden Gophers
b. University of Boston Terriers
c. University of Princeton Tigers
d. University of North Dakota Fighting Sioux

16. Montreal was blessed with such an abundance of talent during their dynasty in the 1970s that they often played games with four forwards on the ice alongside just one defenseman.

    a. True
    b. False

17. Which of the following facts about Canadiens defender Petr Svoboda is NOT true?

    a. He defected to North America from Czechoslovakia.
    b. He drove the Zamboni to clean the ice between periods during his first season.
    c. He scored the gold medal-winning goal for his country in the 1998 Winter Olympics.
    d. He never reached double digit goals in any NHL season.

18. Which Montreal defender scored in a 1-0 victory over the Bruins on November 20, 1928, to record the first-ever NHL goal in Boston Garden?

    a. Francis Bouillon
    b. Ted Harris
    c. Glen Harmon
    d. Sylvio Mantha

19. Which Habs defenseman was the first blueliner in NHL history ever to win a Conn Smythe Trophy as MVP of the playoffs?

    a. Chris Chelios
    b. Larry Robinson
    c. Serge Savard
    d. Émile Bouchard

20. Canadiens defender J.C. Tremblay donated a kidney to his daughter in 1979 and died of kidney cancer in 1994.

    a. True
    b. False

QUIZ ANSWERS

1. C – Detroit's Nicklas Lidstrom

2. A – True

3. D – Most Stanley Cups won by a father and son (9)

4. C – Most penalty minutes recorded by a defenseman

5. B – NASCAR racing

6. B – Larry Robinson

7. A – True

8. D – Éric Desjardins

9. A – Josh Gorges

10. B – Pernell Karl

11. D – 15 seasons

12. A – True

13. B – 6th

14. C – Jeff Petry

15. D – University of North Dakota Fighting Sioux

16. B – False

17. B – He drove the Zamboni to clean the ice between periods during his first season.

18. D – Sylvio Mantha

19. C – Serge Savard

20. A – True

DID YOU KNOW?

1. Andrei Markov was a rock for many years on the Canadiens blue line. He played for 20 years after debuting with Montreal and never skated for another NHL team. Markov did, however, spend some time with five clubs in the AHL, RSL, and KHL.

2. Habs defenseman Guy "Pointu" Lapointe was known both for his excellent play and his sense of humor. He maintains the Canadiens' record for goals in a season by a defender (28), but is perhaps even better remembered for the time he coated his hand with Vaseline before shaking hands with Prime Minister Pierre Trudeau in the Montreal locker room.

3. Terry Harper was an appreciated stay-at-home defenseman with the Canadiens. He was good at clearing creases and killing penalties, but not scoring. His teammates coined the term "Harper hat trick" to reflect when he tallied three goals in an entire season (which happened during five of his 18 seasons).

4. Defenseman Sheldon Souray became such an offensive force for the Canadiens that he set the NHL record for most power-play goals scored by a defender, with 19 in 2006-07. His slapshot was so hard and so feared that he once faked taking one in a shootout and scored the game-winning goal when the goalie could not recover.

5. When defenseman Émile Bouchard played for the Canadiens in the 1940s and '50s, he was six inches taller and 40 pounds heavier than the average player. When combined with his weight-lifting regimen (which was not common among athletes at the time), Bouchard was a fearsome presence league-wide.

6. Star defenseman Jacques Laperrière was well thought of in Montreal even after his playing days ended. He became an assistant head coach with the team and lasted in the position through six different head coaches over a period of 16 years.

7. Canadiens defender and captain Shea Weber has had an illustrious international career that includes gold medals at the World Junior Championships, the World Cup of Hockey, the World Championships, and two at the Winter Olympics.

8. A memorable prank occurred on a night in 1953, when long-time Habs defenseman Émile Bouchard was honored with a new Buick. When Bouchard got in the car to drive it off the ice, he discovered that visiting Detroit captain Ted Lindsay had stolen the keys and stranded Bouchard in front of the crowd. The crowd loved it, and Lindsay eventually returned the keys and congratulated Bouchard.

9. Habs defender P.K. Subban enjoyed showing off his personality and style outside the arena. His fashion sense led to him being named by *Sports Illustrated* as one the 50 best dressed athletes, and he has discussed his hatmaker, tailor, and shoemaker in *GQ* magazine.

10. Defenseman Doug Harvey was one of the league's first offensively minded defensemen. He and his Canadiens power-play unit were so good that they inspired an NHL rule change. After the 1955-56 season, the league ruled that a power play ended after the team with the man advantage had scored. Prior to this, Harvey and his mates would often pot numerous goals after an opponents' penalty.

CHAPTER 10:

CENTERS OF ATTENTION

QUIZ TIME!

1. Canadiens center Brian Skrudland holds the NHL record for the quickest overtime goal scored in the playoffs. How soon into overtime did he put an end to Game 2 of the 1986 Stanley Cup Finals?

    a. 4 minutes, 38 seconds
    b. 2 minutes, 15 seconds
    c. 1 minute, 3 seconds
    d. 9 seconds

2. Canadiens centers have a long-established tradition: when a new pivot joins the club, he must spend his first practice speaking only French or saying nothing at all.

    a. True
    b. False

3. How did Montreal center Jacques Lemaire develop his remarkable slapshot (which was considered to be second best in the NHL, behind only Bobby Hull's)?

a. He used a weightier, steel puck to practice with as a child.

b. He always stayed after practice to fire 50 slapshots before leaving the ice.

c. He practiced shooting from the red line at center ice until he was able to occasionally beat goalies from that distance.

d. He used a hockey stick when driving golf balls off the tee to develop his form.

4. Which Canadiens center became the first athlete born in the 2000s to play in any major professional North American sports league?

a. Nick Suzuki

b. Max Domi

c. Jesperi Kotkaniemi

d. Phillip Danault

5. Which Canadiens center won 10 Stanley Cups with the team as a player and 7 more as a team executive, for the most total championships by anyone in NHL history?

a. Henri Richard

b. Maurice Richard

c. Yvon Cournoyer

d. Jean Béliveau

6. How long did center Saku Koivu's standing ovation from the Molson Centre crowd last when he returned to the ice on April 9, 2002, after beating cancer?

a. 1 minute, 30 seconds

b. 2 minutes

c. 5 minutes, 45 seconds

d. 8 minutes

7. While celebrating a Stanley Cup victory in 1953, Maurice Richard accidentally broke center Elmer Lach's nose with his stick.

a. True

b. False

8. Canadiens center Tomáš Plekanec was well known for which unusual uniform choice?

a. Wearing one red lace and one blue lace in his skates

b. Tucking his jersey in on the left side of his body only

c. Wearing a turtleneck as an undershirt below his jersey

d. Choosing not to wear a jockstrap while playing

9. Habs center Mike Ribeiro was born in Montreal like many other franchise stars, but his origins come from which country much less commonly associated with hockey?

a. Portugal

b. Argentina

c. Thailand

d. Morocco

10. What ended center Pierre Mondou's career with the Canadiens?

a. He held out for a larger salary and was replaced by young center Guy Carbonneau.

b. His wife was diagnosed with cancer, and Mondou retired to attend to her.

c. He was offered a position in broadcasting for a French-Canadian radio station.

d. He was struck with a high stick in the eye by Ulf Samuelsson.

11. According to multiple sources, Canadiens center Billy Reay was the first player to celebrate a goal by doing what?

a. High five a teammate on the bench while skating by

b. Raise his stick and arms into the air

c. Point to the heavens as if to thank the Lord

d. Pump his fist in an uppercut motion

12. Center Pete Mahovlich ("Little M") played with his brother Frank Mahovlich ("Big M") not just in Montreal, but with the Detroit Red Wings as well.

a. True

b. False

13. Which Habs pivot asked for (and usually received) the assignment of playing against superstar Wayne Gretzky when the Canadiens met the Los Angeles Kings in the 1992-93 Stanley Cup Finals?

a. Brian Skrudland

b. Guy Carbonneau

c. Kirk Muller

d. Denis Savard

14. French-language television network RDS hired which retired Montreal center as its hockey analyst?

a. Stéphane Lebeau

b. Stéphane Richer

c. Vincent Damphousse

d. Yanic Perreault

15. Which of the following languages does Belarussian center Alex Galchenyuk NOT speak?

a. English

b. French

c. Russian

d. Italian

16. Montreal captain Saku Koivu set his career high in points with 75 AFTER coming back from knee injuries, a dislocated shoulder, Burkitt's lymphoma, and a detached retina.

a. True

b. False

17. Canadiens center Doug Jarvis never missed a game in his entire NHL career and still holds the record for most consecutive games played. How many in a row did he suit up for?

a. 782 games

b. 853 games

c. 964 games

d. 1,001 games

18. Which of the following was NOT an honor bestowed upon iconic Canadiens pivot Jean Béliveau?

a. Made a Companion of the Order of Canada

b. Picture put on a Canadian postage stamp

c. Knighted by Queen Victoria

d. Name added to Canada's Walk of Fame

19. Although center Ken Mosdell was primarily known for his 12 years with the Habs, he was also the last player before the NHL's 1967 expansion to have played for a non-Original Six NHL team. Which team did he suit up for?

a. Brooklyn Americans

b. Ottawa Senators

c. Pittsburgh Pirates

d. Toronto St. Pats

20. Montreal's decision to claim center Paul Byron off waivers from the Calgary Flames was aided by viewings of a fan-made YouTube video highlighting Byron's missed breakaway attempts.

a. True

b. False

QUIZ ANSWERS

1. D – 9 seconds

2. B – False

3. A – He used a weightier, steel puck to practice with as a child.

4. C – Jesperi Kotkaniemi

5. D – Jean Béliveau

6. D – 8 minutes

7. A – True

8. C – Wearing a turtleneck as an undershirt below his jersey

9. A – Portugal

10. D – He was struck with a high stick in the eye by Ulf Samuelsson.

11. B – Raise his stick and arms into the air

12. A – True

13. B – Guy Carbonneau

14. C – Vincent Damphousse

15. B – French

16. A – True

17. C – 964 games

18. C – Knighted by Queen Victoria

19. A – Brooklyn Americans

20. A – True

DID YOU KNOW?

1. Early era Habs star Howie Morenz led the team in both points and goals for seven straight seasons. Unfortunately, in his final NHL game, an opposing player fell on top of him, breaking his leg in four places. Morenz never left the hospital room he was taken to because he passed away due to complications from the injury.

2. Decorated Habs center Henri Richard scored not one but two Stanley Cup-clinching goals. In 1966, he scored in overtime against the Detroit Red Wings to claim the title, and then one-upped himself in 1971 against the Chicago Blackhawks, when he notched both the game-tying and game-winning goals in Game 7.

3. Six NHL players have scored two Stanley Cup-clinching goals. In addition to Henri Richard, centers Jacques Lemaire and Jean Béliveau also did it for the Montreal Canadiens, as did left winger Toe Blake, who was the first to accomplish the feat.

4. Longtime Habs captain Saku Koivu spoke fluently in English, Finnish, and Swedish, but not French, which was a concern for some in the Montreal market. After being criticized for this, Koivu jokingly responded that he did speak French, but only to his wife during intimate encounters.

5. Two Canadian Prime Ministers made job offers to retired

Habs center Jean Béliveau. Brian Mulroney proffered a Senate appointment and Jean Chrétien put the Governor Generalship of Canada on the table. Béliveau had other priorities, however, and declined both offers.

6. Canadiens center Bobby Smith has had success in most phases of his career. In junior hockey, he outscored Wayne Gretzky for the league's scoring title. He was then drafted into the NHL 1st overall and promptly won the Calder Trophy as rookie of the year. After winning a Stanley Cup with the Habs, he eventually retired and now owns the Halifax Mooseheads of the QMJHL.

7. After 12 seasons and six Stanley Cups with Montreal, center Ralph Backstrom moved to the World Hockey Association for greater financial benefit, and he became part-owner of the Chicago Cougars franchise after leading them in scoring.

8. Center Elmer Lach set the Canadiens' record for most assists in one game, with six. Although this occurred way back in 1943 and Montreal has boasted many juggernaut offenses since that time, no player has matched it since.

9. Very few players have a signature move named for them, but Montreal center Denis Savard did. Broadcaster Danny Gallivan described Savard's habit of spinning 360 degrees with the puck to avoid being checked as a "Savard-ian Spin-o-rama."

10. Habs center Elmer Lach was tough but injury-prone. Without even mentioning the rest of his body, Lach's head

suffered enough: seven broken noses, three broken jaws, and a fractured skull. At one point, his insurance company offered him $17,000 (which could have purchased him a home at the time) just to retire from hockey.

CHAPTER 11:

THE WINGERS TAKE FLIGHT

QUIZ TIME!

1. Which Montreal winger holds the franchise record for youngest age when scoring his first NHL goal, at 18 years, 75 days old?

   a. Jimmy Roberts

   b. Claude Lemieux

   c. Mario Tremblay

   d. Aurèle Joliat

2. Winger Maurice Richard often led the league in goals, but never in points, prompting one teammate to remark, "Maurice wouldn't even pass you the salt."

   a. True

   b. False

3. Which Habs left winger opened a popular tavern in Montreal a few blocks away from the Forum, which operated for over 30 years?

   a. Bob Gainey

   b. Shayne Corson

c. Dick Duff

d. Toe Blake

4. In the famous Game 7 matchup between Montreal and the Boston Bruins in 1979, where Bruins coach Don Cherry accidentally left too many skaters on the ice, which Habs winger scored the overtime goal to send Montreal to the Stanley Cup Finals?

    a. Guy Lafleur

    b. Yvon Lambert

    c. Steve Shutt

    d. Dickie Moore

5. On April 3, 1977, Canadiens left winger Steve Shutt made NHL history by doing what?

    a. Becoming the first player who had played in the league without a helmet to switch to wearing one for protection

    b. Declining to accept the MVP award because he felt that hockey was primarily about team success

    c. Signing a contract that included a no-trade clause

    d. Becoming the first left winger in NHL history to score 60 goals in a season

6. Which Canadiens winger went his entire career without ever recording more than 19 penalty minutes in a season?

    a. Guy Lafleur

    b. Denis Savard

    c. Mats Naslund

    d. Bob Gainey

7. Montreal's Yvon Cournoyer had developed such muscular legs as a young player that he needed to have his pants specially tailored in order to fit into them.

   a. True
   b. False

8. Which Montreal winger's life and hockey career are showcased in a 2011 documentary film called *The Last Gladiators*?

   a. Brendan Gallagher
   b. Maurice Richard
   c. Claude Lemieux
   d. Chris Nilan

9. Which Habs right winger has won more Stanley Cups (9) than anyone else who was not elected to the Hockey Hall of Fame?

   a. Mario Tremblay
   b. Claude Provost
   c. Yvon Cournoyer
   d. Steve Shutt

10. Which of the following is NOT an accurate statistic related to Montreal tough guy Chris Nilan?

   a. He was once assessed a record 10 penalties in a single NHL game.
   b. He is one of just nine NHL players to finish his career with over 3,000 penalty minutes.
   c. He is the only NHL player to ever engage in three

separate fights in one game with an opposing forward, defenseman, and goalie.

d. He holds the NHL record for highest penalty minute average per game (4.42 minutes).

11. Which Habs winger's noted commitment to defense allowed him to play 16 seasons with Montreal, during which he won four consecutive Frank J. Selke Trophies as the best defensive forward in the NHL?

a. Bob Gainey
b. Bert Olmstead
c. Mike Keane
d. Max Pacioretty

12. In a game against the Vancouver Canucks in 2014, winger Max Pacioretty became the first Canadien to be given two penalty shots in the same game. He was stopped by Roberto Luongo on both attempts, but still finished the game with a hat trick.

a. True
b. False

13. One Canadiens winger inspired riots in the streets of Montreal after being suspended by the NHL president in an incident fans felt unfairly targeted francophones. Who was this player?

a. Henri Richard
b. Maurice Richard
c. Guy Lafleur
d. Réjean Houle

14. Which of the following is NOT a true fact about Montreal winger Aurèle Joliat?

   a. He was awarded to the Habs as compensation for the Saskatoon Sheiks signing Newsy Lalonde in 1922.

   b. He recorded the first documented empty net goal in NHL history in 1932.

   c. He refereed Rocket Richard's first NHL game in 1942.

   d. He was awarded the Order of Canada by Prime Minister Louis St. Laurent in 1952.

15. Two former Habs wingers became brothers-in-law when one married the other's sister. Which players were involved?

   a. Benoit Brunet's sister married Claude Lemieux.

   b. Shayne Corson's sister married Darcy Tucker.

   c. Brian Savage's sister married Brian Gionta.

   d. Martin Rucinsky's sister married Richard Zednik.

16. Skilled and tough Habs winger Bernie Geoffrion scored 393 NHL goals, but received even more stitches during his career.

   a. True

   b. False

17. Only one Montreal Canadien played in all eight games of the famous 1972 Summit Series between Canada and the Soviet Union. Who was this player?

   a. Serge Savard

   b. Frank Mahovlich

c. Yvon Cournoyer

d. Pete Mahovlich

18. Which of the following products did the legendary Maurice Richard NOT endorse after his career with the Canadiens?

a. Beer

b. Car batteries

c. Hair dye

d. Condoms

19. What unlikely occupation does Habs legend Guy Lafleur work in during his retirement from hockey?

a. He owns a scuba diving salvage company.

b. He operates a helicopter rental company.

c. He is president and CEO of the Montreal Zoo.

d. He produces signature lines of alcohol, including tequila and vodka.

20. During the height of the disco craze in 1979, Habs winger Guy Lafleur put out an album called *Lafleur*, on which he read instructions for the game of hockey with disco music in the background.

a. True

b. False

QUIZ ANSWERS

1. C – Mario Tremblay

2. A – True

3. D – Toe Blake

4. B – Yvon Lambert

5. D – Becoming the first left winger in NHL history to score 60 goals in a season

6. C – Mats Naslund

7. A – True

8. D – Chris Nilan

9. B – Claude Provost

10. C – He is the only NHL player to ever engage in three separate fights in one game with an opposing forward, defenseman, and goalie.

11. A – Bob Gainey

12. A – True

13. B – Maurice Richard

14. D – He was awarded the Order of Canada by Prime Minister Louis St. Laurent in 1952.

15. B – Shayne Corson's sister married Darcy Tucker.

16. A – True

17. C – Yvon Cournoyer

18. D – Condoms

19. B – He operates a helicopter rental company.

20. A – True

DID YOU KNOW?

1. In the days before helmets, winger Aurèle Joliat was known for wearing a black cap on his head while he played. Though he retired in the 1930s, Joliat took a few laps around the Montreal Forum ice for fans in 1985 and waved in his hand the same black cap he had worn as a player.

2. Left winger Babe Siebert had a wife, Bernice, who became a paraplegic after problems arose during the birth of the couple's second daughter. Prior to every home game at the Montreal Forum, Siebert would carry Bernice to her seat, and then lift her out of it afterward.

3. Among a long line of Canadiens players known for their style and skill, winger Steve Shutt made a career out of scoring "garbage goals." Shutt didn't always make it pretty, but had excellent positioning, spatial awareness, and hand-eye coordination and boasted an array of talented shots, which allowed him to top the 30-goal mark nine times in his career.

4. Habs winger Bernie Geoffrion married the daughter of Canadiens legend Howie Morenz, Marlene. Their son, Dan, played for the Canadiens in 1979-80, and Dan's son, Blake, joined the team in 2011-12, making him the first-ever fourth-generation NHL player, and linking all four generations to the Montreal franchise.

5. Canadiens left winger Bobby Rousseau played for Montreal during 10 seasons and is remembered for winning four Stanley Cups with the team, as well as scoring five goals in a single game in 1964. Less well-remembered are Rousseau's brothers, Guy and Rollie. Both also played in the NHL for Montreal, but Guy lasted just four games with the team and Rollie only two games.

6. In 2011, Habs winger Max Pacioretty was on the receiving end of a massive hit by massive Boston Bruins defenseman Zdeno Chara. Pacioretty smashed into a stanchion near the end of a bench and was stretchered off the ice with a concussion and fractured vertebra. The hit led to a criminal investigation by police in Montreal, but Pacioretty forgave Chara and returned the following year to win the NHL's Bill Masterton Trophy for perseverance and dedication to hockey.

7. Canadiens icon Maurice Richard set many firsts in the NHL. Among these, he was the first to score 50 goals in a season and the first to score 500 goals in a career. Later, he was also the first non-politician given the honor of a state funeral in the province of Quebec.

8. Three NHL players have returned to play after being inducted into the Hockey Hall of Fame, and Habs winger Guy Lafleur is one of them. Lafleur had retired after clashing with coach Jacques Lemaire. He had asked general manager Serge Savard for a trade, but was denied because Savard did not want to face the ire of angry fans for trading a franchise icon.

9. When Habs winger Dickie Moore broke his wrist during the 1957-58 season, he was a leading contender for the scoring title and Art Ross Trophy. He played the second half of the season with his wrist in a cast, and not only won that scoring title, but helped his line mate Henri Richard finish second in the race.

10. Winger Max Pacioretty (who wore jersey number 67) was such a hit in Montreal that McDonald's restaurants in the province of Quebec honored him in 2016 with a burger called the "Max 67."

CHAPTER 12:

COACHES, GMS, & OWNERS

QUIZ TIME!

1. Who served as the Canadiens' first general manager?

    a. The tandem of Joseph Cattarinich and Jack Laviolette
    b. George Kennedy
    c. Léo Dandurand
    d. The tandem of Cecil Hart and Jules Dugal

2. Scotty Bowman would go on to coach Montreal defenseman Jean-Guy Talbot, the player whose slash fractured Bowman's skull and ended his playing career.

    a. True
    b. False

3. The Canadiens' first NHL head coach, Newsy Lalonde, lasted for how long in that position with the franchise?

    a. 38 games
    b. 95 games
    c. 176 games
    d. 360 games

4. What is legendary Habs coach Scotty Bowman's real first name?

    a. William
    b. Ralph
    c. Benjamin
    d. Scott

5. Who has been the majority owner of the Montreal Canadiens franchise for the longest amount of time?

    a. George Gillett Jr.
    b. Canadian Arena Company
    c. George Kendall-Kennedy
    d. Molson Breweries

6. Which of the following is NOT a true fact about Canadiens coach Scotty Bowman?

    a. He won 14 total Stanley Cups as a coach or front office executive.
    b. He holds the NHL records for coaching victories in both the regular season and the playoffs.
    c. He has won at least one Stanley Cup in every decade since the 1970s.
    d. He owns the records for most wins in a season (62) and fewest losses in a season (8).

7. Center Henri Richard centered a line with his brother Maurice on the wing, despite a fifteen-year age difference between the two.

    a. True
    b. False

8. How many Montreal general managers once skated as players on the team before getting the chance to guide it from the front office?

   a. 0
   b. 3
   c. 6
   d. 9

9. Which coach led the Canadiens to their first Stanley Cup championship?

   a. Jules Dugal
   b. Babe Siebert
   c. Newsy Lalonde
   d. Léo Dandurand

10. How many of the Canadiens' 24 head coaches (not counting "interim" coaches) have spent their entire NHL coaching career with Montreal?

    a. 2
    b. 4
    c. 8
    d. 12

11. Who is Montreal's leader in all-time coaching wins with the franchise?

    a. Toe Blake
    b. Dick Irvin
    c. Scotty Bowman
    d. Cecil Hart

12. Montreal is the only NHL franchise to have a player rise from skating for the team to ownership of the team.

    a. True
    b. False

13. Franchise legend Henri Richard called which bench boss "the worst coach I have ever played for," leading to the coach being demoted to junior hockey even after winning the Stanley Cup with Montreal?

    a. Toe Blake
    b. Al MacNeil
    c. Dick Irvin
    d. Claude Ruel

14. In which of the following locations did Jacques Lemaire NOT coach a team?

    a. Switzerland
    b. Montreal
    c. State University of New York College at Plattsburgh
    d. Los Angeles

15. Which Canadiens general manager has led the franchise to the most playoff appearances?

    a. Léo Dandurand
    b. Sam Pollock
    c. Frank J. Selke
    d. Tommy Gorman

16. Canadiens owner George N. Gillett Jr. once proposed trading franchises with Manchester United owner Malcolm Glazer as part of a business deal.

a. True

b. False

17. Legendary coach Scotty Bowman has won the most Stanley Cup championships (9) in the NHL's coaching history. How do his victories break down?

    a. 4 with Montreal, 2 with Pittsburgh, 2 with Detroit

    b. 1 with St. Louis, 3 with Montreal, 2 with Pittsburgh, 3 with Detroit

    c. 5 with Montreal, 1 with Pittsburgh, 3 with Detroit

    d. 7 with Montreal, 1 with Pittsburgh, 1 with Detroit

18. How did J. David Molson, William A. Molson, and Peter B. Molson become the owners of the Montreal Canadiens?

    a. They purchased the team when the previous owner passed away.

    b. They inherited the team from their father.

    c. As minority owners, they bought out the shares of five other owners.

    d. They purchased the club from their cousins.

19. Which Canadiens coaches have won the Jack Adams Award as the league's top coach?

    a. Toe Blake, Scotty Bowman, and Alain Vigneault

    b. Dick Irvin, Bob Gainey, and Claude Julien

    c. Scotty Bowman and Pat Burns

    d. Al MacNeil and Jacques Demers

20. Initially, coach Toe Blake rejected goalie Jacques Plante's request to wear a mask during games, but changed his mind after Plante broke his nose stopping a shot.

a. True
b. False

QUIZ ANSWERS

1. A – The tandem of Joseph Cattarinich and Jack Laviolette

2. B – False

3. B – 95 games

4. A – William

5. D – Molson Breweries

6. C – He has won at least one Stanley Cup in every decade since the 1970s.

7. A – True

8. B – 3

9. D – Léo Dandurand

10. C – 8

11. A – Toe Blake

12. B – False

13. B – Al MacNeil

14. D – Los Angeles

15. C – Frank J. Selke

16. B – False

17. C – 5 with Montreal, 1 with Pittsburgh, 3 with Detroit

18. D – They purchased the club from their cousins.

19. C – Scotty Bowman and Pat Burns

20. A – True

DID YOU KNOW?

1. Canadiens general manager Frank Selke made one of the most legendary moves in NHL history to get superstar Jean Béliveau onto the team. Béliveau had signed a contract saying he would play with the Habs if he ever played professional hockey, but he happily spent multiple seasons playing as an amateur instead. Finally, Selke convinced the Habs' owners to buy the entire amateur league and convert it to a professional one, at which point Béliveau had no choice but to join the Montreal lineup.

2. Ex-Habs player Babe Siebert was named coach of the Canadiens in 1939. Unfortunately, Siebert never got the chance to step behind the bench for the team because he drowned in Lake Huron before the season began. Montreal hired another of its former players, Pit Lepine, to replace Siebert as coach.

3. After his playing days, Jacques Lemaire became a successful coach, not just with Montreal, but also in New Jersey, where he won a Stanley Cup with the Devils. Although he was known for his controversial "neutral zone trap" system, which slowed down the game considerably, Lemaire's Devils did finish second in league scoring in 1993-94.

4. Habs coach Mario Tremblay had a running feud with goaltender Patrick Roy that eventually led to Roy's trade

to the Colorado Avalanche. The feud was marked by incidents such as a near fist-fight in a coffee shop, Roy's laughter at Tremblay's lack of coaching background, Tremblay's slapshot toward Roy's throat at a team practice, and Tremblay's refusal to pull Roy from the net despite a nine-goal shellacking against the Detroit Red Wings.

5. Montreal was famous for hiring their former players as head coaches. They had enough success doing so that some other teams in the league tried to copy this strategy. In the span of a decade, for example, the New York Rangers hired three ex-Montreal players (Bernie Geoffrion, John Ferguson, and Jean-Guy Talbot) to coach their team.

6. Three men have served as both coach and general manager of the Montreal Canadiens: Léo Dandurand, Cecil Hart, and Jules Dugal. More recently, Bob Gainey did as well, but as general manager, he named himself interim head coach twice without ever taking on the position full time.

7. Habs coach Toe Blake has recorded the most Stanley Cup victories as the team's bench boss, with eight championships, including five in a row during his first five seasons, which remains an NHL record.

8. Réjean Houle was an excellent player for the Canadiens, but not such a great general manager. During his tenure, he traded away popular players such as Patrick Roy, Vincent Damphousse, Mark Recchi, Mike Keane, and

Pierre Turgeon, without getting much in return. He also struggled to lure free agents to Montreal and to unearth young talent in the draft.

9. Although many previous Montreal general managers might have been awarded the NHL General Manager of the Year Trophy, the award was only founded in 2010 and has yet to be won by a Canadiens GM.

10. Former Habs winger Bob Gainey was a man of many roles. He became the team's general manager in 2003. During his tenure, he fired two Habs coaches, Claude Julien and Guy Carbonneau (who had been a Habs player as well), and stepped in to coach the team himself.

CHAPTER 13:

THE AWARDS SECTION

QUIZ TIME!

1. Which Hab has won the most Hart Trophies as league MVP while playing for Montreal?

   a. Maurice Richard

   b. Guy Lafleur

   c. Jean Béliveau

   d. Howie Morenz

2. The first Canadien to win any major award given out by the NHL was franchise center Elmer Lach.

   a. True

   b. False

3. The Presidents' Trophy for leading the NHL in points was introduced in 1985-86. How many times have the Montreal Canadiens won it?

   a. 0

   b. 1

   c. 2

   d. 3

4. Which Habs player won 11 Stanley Cup championships, which is a record not just for the team or the NHL, but for any athlete in North American professional sports (tied with Boston Celtic Bill Russell)?

   a. Jean Béliveau
   b. Larry Robinson
   c. Henri Richard
   d. Bernie Geoffrion

5. Why did Montreal center Saku Koivu win the NHL's King Clancy Memorial Trophy?

   a. Leading the league in penalty minutes drawn against opponents
   b. Founding the Saku Koivu Foundation for charity
   c. Having the highest plus/minus rating of any forward throughout the season
   d. Receiving the most three-star votes after games

6. Since 2006, the NHL has given out the Mark Messier Leadership Award. Which Montreal Canadien has been honored as its winner?

   a. Saku Koivu
   b. Shea Weber
   c. Carey Price
   d. None of them has won it.

7. The Montreal Canadiens will always be the all-time leader in O'Brien Trophy wins, with 11, since the trophy itself has been retired.

a. True

b. False

8. Who was the most recent Montreal player to make the NHL All-Rookie Team?

a. Jesperi Kotkaniemi

b. Brendan Gallagher

c. P.K. Subban

d. Carey Price

9. Which two Habs goaltenders shared the franchise's first-ever William M. Jennings Trophy for allowing the fewest goals?

a. Ken Dryden and Michel Larocque

b. Patrick Roy and Brian Hayward

c. Carey Price and Cristobal Huet

d. Rick Wamsley and Denis Herron

10. Which of these Canadiens icons was the first player ever awarded the Art Ross Trophy as the league's leading scorer?

a. Dickie Moore

b. Jean Béliveau

c. Elmer Lach

d. Bernie Geoffrion

11. The Lady Byng Memorial Trophy for sportsmanship, gentlemanly conduct, and playing ability has been won twice in Montreal's franchise history. Which player won it while recording only a single minor penalty all season?

a. Toe Blake

b. Mats Naslund

c. Stéphane Richer

d. Denis Savard

12. No Montreal Canadien has ever won the award for scoring the most goals in an NHL season, which is named for franchise icon Maurice "Rocket" Richard.

a. True

b. False

13. Which of the following Habs players won the Calder Memorial Trophy as the league's top rookie?

a. Maurice Richard

b. Jean Béliveau

c. Johnny Quilty

d. P.K. Subban

14. Of the Canadiens in the Hockey Hall of Fame, Georges Vézina is first among them to skate with the Habs. What year did he begin playing with the team?

a. 1910

b. 1917

c. 1922

d. 1928

15. Which Canadiens goalie holds the NHL record for most goals allowed during the league's All-Star Games?

a. Patrick Roy

b. Jacques Plante

c. Carey Price

d. Ken Dryden

16. The Montreal Canadiens have had more players elected to the Hockey Hall of Fame than any other NHL franchise.

a. True

b. False

17. The James Norris Trophy, given annually to the NHL's best defenseman, has been won by how many Montreal Canadiens throughout the years?

a. 3

b. 6

c. 9

d. 12

18. How many Montreal Canadiens have been elected to the Hall of Fame in the builders category?

a. 2

b. 5

c. 10

d. 15

19. How many times has Montreal hosted the NHL's annual All-Star Game?

a. 0

b. 4

c. 7

d. 12

20. Defenseman Doug Harvey won six James Norris Trophies with Montreal, which remains an NHL record for a player/team combination.

    a. True
    b. False

QUIZ ANSWERS

1. D – Howie Morenz

2. B – False

3. A – 0

4. C – Henri Richard

5. B – Founding the Saku Koivu Foundation for charity

6. D – None of them has won it.

7. A – True

8. B – Brendan Gallagher

9. D – Rick Wamsley and Denis Herron

10. C – Elmer Lach

11. A – Toe Blake

12. A – True

13. C – Johnny Quilty

14. A – 1910

15. A – Patrick Roy

16. B – False

17. B – 6

18. C – 10

19. D – 12

20. B – False

DID YOU KNOW?

1. The Bill Masterton Trophy for perseverance, sportsmanship, and dedication to hockey has been won five times by a Montreal Canadien (tied for the NHL record with the New York Rangers). Right winger Claude Provost was the first-ever recipient of the award, and was followed by Henri Richard, Serge Savard, Saku Koivu, and Max Pacioretty.

2. Two members of the Montreal Canadiens were included in the original nine-person Hockey Hall of Fame class that was inducted in 1945. Both Howie Morenz and Georges Vézina were included and have since been joined by many other Habs.

3. The Vezina Trophy, given annually to the NHL's best goaltender, was donated to the league after former Montreal goaltender Georges Vézina passed away. It has been won a record 36 times by a Canadiens goalie, most recently by Carey Price in 2014-15.

4. The Hockey Hall of Fame normally requires a waiting period of three years after a player is retired for him to be considered for enshrinement. On 10 occasions, that waiting period has been waived for "exceptional players." Twice this has been done for Montreal Canadiens; first for Maurice "Rocket" Richard and then for Jean Béliveau.

5. The Frank J. Selke Trophy, given each year to the forward

who best exhibits defensive prowess, was created for the 1977-78 NHL season. Montreal forward Bob Gainey promptly won the award four seasons in a row.

6. Montreal's 24 Stanley Cup championships remain by far the most in NHL history, as second place Toronto is 11 cups behind. Among non-Original Six teams, Pittsburgh and Edmonton are closest, with 5 apiece.

7. The very first time the NHL awarded the Conn Smythe Trophy for most valuable player in the playoffs, it went to a Montreal Canadien. Jean Béliveau took home the honor after the Habs won the Stanley Cup in 1965.

8. NHL players vote annually on the Ted Lindsay Award (formerly the Lester B. Pearson Award) for the most valuable player in each season. Four Montreal Canadiens have been so honored, including Guy Lafleur's three consecutive wins between 1975 and 1978.

9. The Lester Patrick Trophy is awarded each year for outstanding service to hockey in the United States (making it naturally difficult for a Canadian to win). Nevertheless, Habs icon Scotty Bowman had such a distinguished career even outside Montreal that he was given the award in 2001.

10. Habs goalie Carey Price had a massive 2015 season. During that year, he became the only goaltender in NHL history to win the William M. Jennings Trophy, the Vezina Trophy, the Hart Trophy, and the Ted Lindsay Trophy in the same season.

CONCLUSION

There you have it; an amazing collection of Canadiens trivia, information, and statistics at your fingertips! Regardless of how you fared on the quizzes, we hope that you found this book entertaining, enlightening, and educational.

Ideally, you knew many of these details, but also learned a good deal more about the history of the Montreal Canadiens, their players, coaches, management, and some of the quirky stories surrounding the team. If you got a little peek into the colorful details that make being a fan so much more enjoyable, then mission accomplished!

The good news is that the trivia doesn't have to stop there! Spread the word. Challenge your fellow Habs fans to see if they can do any better. Share some of the stories with the next generation to help them become Montreal supporters too.

If you are a big enough Canadiens fan, consider creating your own quiz with some of the details you know that weren't presented here and then test your friends to see if they can match your knowledge.

The Montreal Canadiens are a storied franchise. They have a long history with multiple periods of success (and a few that were less than successful). They've had glorious superstars, iconic moments, hilarious tales…but, most of all, they have wonderful, passionate fans. Thank you for being one of them.

Manufactured by Amazon.ca
Bolton, ON